T.JOHNSON.

CHARLES GOUNOD

From a photograph taken in 1859, about the time of the first production of
Faust, Gounod being then in his forty-first year.

G. SCHIRMER'S
COLLECTION
OF
OPERAS.

FAUST

A Lyric Drama in Five Acts

BY

JULES BARBIER AND MICHEL CARRÉ

(English Version by H. T. Chorley)

MUSIC BY

CHARLES GOUNOD

*Carefully Revised after the Latest Editions, and Containing
the Complete Ballet-Music*

Pr. in Paper $1.50
Pr. in Cloth $2.50

G. SCHIRMER ~ NEW YORK.

INDEX.

IV

FAUST.

CHARACTERS OF THE DRAMA,

With the original cast as presented at the first performance, at the Théâtre Lyrique, Paris, on March 19, 1859.

FAUST....................	*Tenor*..........	M. BARBOT.
MEPHISTOPHELES............	*Bass*..........	M. BALANQUÉ.
VALENTINE.............	*Baritone*..........	M. ISMAËL.
MARGARITA	*Soprano*..........	MME. MIOLAN-CARVALHO.
SIEBEL..................	*Mezzo-Soprano*....	MLLE. FAIVRE.
MARTHA................	*Mezzo-Soprano*.....	MME. DUCLOS.

THE STORY OF FAUST.

The "Faust legend," on which Goethe's dramatic poem is based, gradually gathered round the nucleus afforded by the life and deeds of Dr. Johann Faust, a German scholar whose career can be traced, with more or less certainty, from about 1507 to 1540.

This "historical" Faust was an adventurer, whose fame as an alchemist and astrologer, physician and adept in the black art, spread by the credulous and by his own travels through Germany, attained to vast proportions. His native country is variously stated as Swabia, Saxony, and Poland. He was known as the "Philosopher of Philosophers;" he professed ability to revive the New Testament miracles, and asserted that the victories won by the imperial armies in Italy were due to his supernatural influence. The popular imagination naturally seized and enlarged upon the supernatural in Faust's career ; and these tales, with the addition of traditions of wonders performed by the earlier professors of magic, crystallizing about this central modern figure, constituted the elements out of which three distinct versions of Faust's life arose in the German folk-lore of the 16th century.

In literature, Faust appears for the first time in 1587, when the "Historia of Dr. Johann Fausten, the world-renowned Magician and Necromancer," was published at Frankfort-on-the-Main. He is described as a student of theology at Wittenberg, who, after taking his degree, becomes a man of the world, a doctor of medicine, an astrologer and mathematician. He sells his soul to Satan to obtain supernatural power, which he enjoys for 24 years, when the devil claims him, and kills him, in a village near Wittenberg, by throwing him at night from one side to the other against the walls, and casts his dead body on a dunghill, where it is found the next morning.

It is altogether probable, that from this earliest printed version Marlowe took the idea for his "Life and Death of Dr. Faustus" (1588), the first dramatization of the legend, which lays more stress on Faust's desire for earthly pleasures than on his longing for wisdom. It was followed, during the next two centuries, by many different versions and modifications of the story, chiefly by German writers. Marlowe's drama made its way back to Germany in translations, and became, with various additions and adaptations, a genuine popular stage-piece. In the course of time it passed into the possession of the puppet-show; and is now rarely seen, in its popular form, on even the humblest of German stages.

Goethe's Faust-drama lifts the hero far above the plane of individual limitation, and makes of him the typical representative of all humanity, with its yearnings and aspirations, its frailties and sorrows. The vastness of its ideal scope rendered it impossible to construct a drama in which the unities should be observed with any semblance of strictness. It is a series of scenes and episodes, among which the only one that is carried to a natural, logical, inexorable "dramatic" conclusion is the episode of Faust's love for Gretchen. It is upon this episode that Gounod's librettists, Carré and Barbier, founded their text. From the nature of the case, they were obliged to prune and rearrange their model.

In the opera, Faust is presented as a scholar past the meridian of life, who, weary of book-wisdom and solitary study, and heart-sick at the fruitlessness of his striving to fathom the secrets of Nature and the spirit-world, is in the act of raising a poisoned draught to his lips, when his hand is arrested by the tones of a gay chorus outside. Overcome by bitterly regretful memories, he curses the delusion which has caused him to waste his best years in efforts to learn the unknowable; and, having lost all hope of heaven, in a frenzy of despair he calls on Satan to aid him. The spirit of evil, in the form of Mephistopheles, appears. Faust adjures him to restore his youth and the delights of love, and, lured by a vision of beauty (Margaret) which the tempter causes to appear, readily signs the compact for which the wily Mephistopheles stipulates. Act II begins with the kaleidoscopic scenes of the "Kermesse," or annual fair and festival of the town; Scene 2 introduces Valentine, Margaret's brother, and Wagner (soldiers about to depart for the wars), and Siebel, a youth who secretly loves Margaret. Wagner, striking up a jolly song to drown the grief of leave-taking, is abruptly interrupted by Mephistopheles, who sings a "better" song, tells of disasters threatening his auditors, conjures forth wine from the cask which serves as the tavern-sign, and finishes by insultingly drinking the health of Margaret. Set upon by the incensed brother and lover, he

baffles their attack by magic art. Faust now insists on meeting the Margaret of his vision; she soon passes by, he accosts her, and is repulsed. This still further inflames his ardor; in Act III he enters her chamber during her absence, and leaves there a casket of jewels. Margaret finds them on her return, and, while delightedly adorning herself, is surprised by Dame Martha, a neighbor, who overcomes her scruples at taking the present, and extols her good fortune in having so generous a lover. Mephistopheles and Faust now appear. The former engages Dame Martha in conversation, thus permitting Faust to make advances to Margaret; he wins her heart in a series of beautiful love-scenes. Act IV shows Margaret abandoned by Faust, a prey to sinister forebodings, and scoffed at by her former companions. Valentine returns, discovers what has occurred during his absence, and vows vengeance; meeting Faust and Mephistopheles together, while the latter is addressing a mocking serenade to Margaret, a combat ensues, and Valentine falls mortally wounded. His assailants escape from the town. Aroused by the noise of the affray, the neighbors, and with them his sister, gather around the dying soldier, whose last breath is a curse upon Margaret for her frailty. In the terrible church-scene Mephistopheles, invisible, nears Margaret, who is seeking consolation in prayer, and by his whispered threats of vengeance to come causes the unhappy girl to sink in a swoon of anguish. In Act V, Margaret is in prison, having killed her child in a delirious agony of remorse and self-reproach. Mephistopheles puts the warder to sleep, and obtains his keys for Faust, who thus gains access to his beloved, and implores her to flee with him from the impending death-sentence; but, bereft of reason by her sufferings, she cannot be prevailed upon to go, and at sight of Mephistopheles, who enters to urge haste, and whom she instinctively regards as the real author of her woes, her horror reaches its climax, and she sinks lifeless to the ground. An angelic chorus proclaims her "saved;" and Mephistopheles, cheated of her soul, vanishes with Faust.

"Faust."

Introduction.

Adagio molto, quasi largo.

CHAS. GOUNOD.

11947

Nº 1. Solo and Chorus.

(Curtain rises.) (Faust discovered, sitting at a table covered with parchments.)

Faust.

No!
Vain!

in-ter-ro-go in-van, im-mer-so ne-gli stu-di, la na-
in vain do I call, thro'-out my vig-il wea-ry, On cre-

6 Allegretto.

Già sor-ge il dì; già vien l'al-ba no - vel-la, e spa-rir
The stars grow pale; The dawn cov-ers the heav-en, Mys-te-rious

11947

fa l'o-scu-ri-tà! an-cora un dì, an-co-ra un dì spun-
night pass-es a - way! An-oth-er day! And yet an-oth-er

tò! O mor - te, af-fret-ta il vol, per dar-mi al fin ri-
day! O Death! come, in pit - y, come, and bid the strife be

Allegro.

po _ so! Eb _ ben! ses _ sa fug-ge da
o _ ver! What then? if Death thus will a-

me, per-chè non va-do in con - tro a le - i?
void me, Why should I not go forth and seek him?

tin - vo - la a me! _____ va via, _____ va
Pass on your way, _____ go by, _____ go

pp   *ppp*

Andante.

via! _____ Cop - pa de - gli a - vi
by! _____ Gob - let so oft - en

Tromboni, etc.

f   *fp*

miei già tan - te vol - te col - ma, per - chè tre - mi tu in mia
drain'd by my fa - ther's hand so stead - y, Why now dost thou trem - ble in

fp   *fp*

Allegretto.

man? per - chè tre - mi tu in mia man? _____
mine? Why now _____ dost thou trem - ble in mine? _____

Ob., Clar., & Fag.

cresc.   *f*   *f*

Chorus (behind the scenes.)   TENORS.   *p*

L'au - ro - ra ai cam - pi or - mai ci ap-
Come forth, ye reap - ers, young and

BASSES.   *p*

L'au - ro - ra ai cam - pi or - mai ci ap-
Come forth, ye reap - ers, young and

Viols.

p

14

Nº 2. Scena and Duet.

co - ra, che sen va più bre - ve dell' o - ra, so - gni d'a-
lure me, Yet when pos - sest no rapture could se - cure me! From dreams of

mor, fas - tied o - nor! Ma - le - di - coil pia - cer, ma - le - di - co la
Hope! Am - bi - tions high! and their hap - pi - ness rare! Accurst my vaunted

scien - za, la pre-ghie - ra e la fè! È stan-ca al - fin la mia pa-
learn - ing, And for-give - ness and pray'r! Accurst the pa - tience in my

zien - za! A me, Sa - tan! ___ a me! ___ I cry! ___ Wind.
yearn - ing! To pow'rs of ill ___ I cry! ___

Maestoso. **Mephistopheles** (appearing suddenly.)

So - no quì!
I re - ply!

Per - chè tal sor
You stare as you

Fl. & Viols.

18

11947

tan es-ser più cor - te - - - se im - por - ta, E che mestier non
skill, That you should po - lite - - - ly treat me; And not as you have

e - ra di far - lo viag-giar tan - to per dir-gli po - i;
done to - day, Call for aid from far a - way Then to say "Be-

Faust.

E che puoi
Canst thou do

"quel - la è la por - ta!" **Allegro.**
gone!" as if to beat me!

f Viols.

tu per me?
aught for me?

Meph.

Tut - to! tut-to! ma prì-ma mi dì che bra-mi
Can I! All but first let me hear what I must

p

sor che as-sai più val!
store what out-buys them all!

io bra - mo la gio-vi -
My youth! canst thou re -

Allegro, ben marcato.

nez - za!____ Io vo - glio il pia -
store me!____ Be mine____ the de -

Brass.

ff   p   dim.   p

cer,____ Le bel - le don - zel - le! Ne vo'____ le ca -
light____ Of Beau - ty's ca - ress - es, Her soft____ wav-y

Viol.

rez - ze, Ne vo - glio i pen - sier!_____ Bru -
tress - es, Her smile____ beam-ing bright!____ Be

cia - - re vo - gl'i - o d'in so - li to ar -
mine____ the warm cur - rent of blood in ev - 'ry

cresc.

dor,___ Il gau - dio de - si - o Dei sen - sie del
vein,___ The pas - sion in tor - rent, Which noth - ing can

cor!___ Oh vien __ gio - vi - nez - za, Ch'io tor - nia go-
rein,___ The rapt - ure whose pleas - ure To Time __ giv-eth

der!___ Mi ren - di l'eb - brez - za, Mi ren - dii l pia-
flight,___ O youth __ with-out meas - ure, Be mine __ thy de-

cer!___ Al co - re l'eb - brez - za, Ai sen-
light!___ O youth with-out meas - ure, Be mine,___

-sii l pia - cer!___ Sta ben!___ sta ben!___ sta
be mine thy de - light!___ 'Tis well!___ 'tis well!___ 'tis

Meph.

colla voce.   *a tempo.* **p**   Fl. & Viol.

11947

ben!___ sta ben! io vo'___ far pa-goil tuo_ ca-
well!___ 'tis well! Be young_ and en - joy___ with-out

'Celli.

pric - cio, io vo'___ far pa-goil tuo ca-pric-
meas - ure. I will___ con-tent your wild-est crav-

poco rit.

Faust.

cio. Ed___ in pre-mio che bra___ mi da
ing. And___ what fee do you ask___ in ex-

Fl., Clar., etc.

a tempo. sfz   p   p

Meph.

me?___ Tel_ di - rò; po - co io
change?___ What? my fee? Hard-ly worth

pp

vo'___ al tuo co-mand oor quì son i -
hav-ing_ Fl. On earth I will wait_ on your pleas -

Wind.

f Maestoso.

Faust.

o,
Ma lag-giù
al mio sa-rai tu! Lag-giù!

ure,
But be-low
you must wait on me! Be-low!

Tromba.

Più animato.

Meph.

Lag-giù!
an-diam,

Be-low!
come on!

scri-vi!
e che, la man tre-ma?

sign-it!
How now? what af-frights you?

E per-chè tan-to ti-tu-bar?
La gio-ven-tù t'in-

Do you trem-ble wav-er-ing in fear?
See how fair youth in-

riten.

vi-vi-ta;
o-sa-la con-tem-

vites you!
See what I show you

Viols.

11947

26

11947

Meph. (taking the goblet.)

Ed or, Si - gno - - re,
For the rest of the chap - - ter,

il cen - - no mio t'in -
'Tis I who wait up -

vi - - ta a li - bar que - sto
on you To drain from yon

nap - - po
gob - - let
o -
The

ve fu - man - do sta mor - te non più,
nec - tar of the sun, No more of Death

(Faust drains the goblet, and is transformed into a young man.)

(The vision vanishes.) Allegro, ben moderato.
Meph.

Vien!___
Come!___

Faust.

E la ri - ve - drò?___   Quan-do?
I'll meet her a - gain?___   When, tho'?

Si - cu - ro!   Que - sto
No ques - tion!   Why, to-

Sta   ben!___   An -
A - way!___   a -

dì!___   An - dia - mo!   An -
day!___   A - way,   then!   a -

34

vo - glio l'eb - brez - - - za, Ne
youth with - out meas - - - ure, Be

vo - glio l'eb - brez - - - za, Per
youth with - out meas - - - ure, Be

vo',_____ ne vo'
mine,_____ be mine

te,_____ per te_____
thine,_____ be thine_____

il pia - cer!_____
thy de light._____

il pia - cer!_____
the de light._____

End of Act I.

Act II.
Nº 3. Grand Chorus._ The Fair. (La Kermesse.)

Allegretto.

Piano.

(Curtain rises.)

(Students.)

Chorus. 1st BASSES. *mf*

Sù,   da   be - re, Sù   da   ber,   Un bic -
Still   or sparkling, Rough or fine! What can it

chie - re A ___ me! Lie - to in __ co - re Tra - can -
mat-ter, So we have wine? What if the vin-tage Great be or

Wagner. (Solo.)

nar, Il li - quo - re __ Si __ dè! Si, la __ go - la In-naf-
small, Your jol-ly to-per Drink-eth of all. Stu - dent vers'd in ev-'ry __

Fag.

stacc.

fiam, L'ac - qua __ so - la Sprez-ziam. Quà un bic - chie - re Di li -
bar-rel, Save wa - ter bright, To __ thy __ glo - ry, to __ thy __

Fl. etc.

Chorus. 1st BASSES.

cor, Vo - glio be - re An - cor! So - lo il vi - no, L'acqua __
love, Drink a - way _____ to - night! Stu - dent vers'd in ev-'ry __

no, È di-vi-no. Be-viam. Quà un bic-chie-re Dì li-
bar-rel, Save wa-ter bright, To thy glo-ry, to thy

cor, Vo-glio be-re, An-cor!
love, Drink a-way to-night!

Horn.

Cor. à pistons.

2nd BASSES. (Soldiers.)

Don-ze-le o cit-ta-
Young girls, an-cient

Bassi, Fag. etc.

del - le,   U - na   co - sa son!   Vin - cia - mo ed e - spu-
castles,   They are all   the same,   Old   towns,   dain - ty___

gnia-mo   bel - le e ba - stion!   Il prez-zo del_____ ri - scatto,
maid-ens,   Are a - like our game!   For the he - ro,   brave and ten-der,

Do - vran - no_ pa - gar,   A que - sto so - lo pat - to
Makes   of_ both his prey!   Both to val - or   must sur - ren - der,

Vo - gliam pu - gnar!   Vo - gliam pu - gnar!
And a_ ran - som pay!   And a_ ran - som pay!

Cor. à pistons.

Horn.

1st TENORS. (Burghers.)

Nei dì di ri - po - so e di fe-sta,
Each new Sunday brings the old sto-ry,

Di guerre ed' ar - mi a - mo par - lar; Men - tre la gen - te
Dan - ger gone by, How we en - joy! While to - day each

a me-di-tar Si stan - ca la te - sta, Men vo'a se-der
hot - headed boy Fights for to-day's lit-tle glo - ry! Let me but sit

sul pon-ti - cel, E là tran-quil-lo amo ve - de - re, Ve-
co - sy and dry, Un - der the trees with my daugh - ter,

ni - re e an-da - re bar-chi e bat-tel, Vo-tan - do, vo-tan-do il bic-
And while raft and boat trav-el by, I drink to the folk on the

chie - re! Men vo'a se - der sul pon-ti-cel, E là se-duto a-mo ve-
wa - ter! Let me but sit Co - sy and dry, Un - der the trees with my

de - re, Ve - ni - re e anda - re barchi e battel, Vo-tan-do, vo-tan-do il bic-
daugh - ter,___ And while raft and boat travel by, I drink to the folk on the

chie - re!
wa - ter!

f

1st SOPRANOS. (Girls.)

Non ve-de-te i bei gar-zo - - - ni S'a-van-zan di
On-ly look how they do eye us, Yon-der fel-lows

Viol⁵

42

là, Per ma-ri-ti so-no buo- - - - ni, Re -stiamo un po'
gay! How-so-ev-er they de -fy_____ us, Nev-er run a-

quà, Re - stiamo un po' quà, re - stia - mo un po'
way, Nev - er run a -way, nev - ér_____ run a -

2nd TENORS. (Young Students.)

quà_
way!

Non ve - de - te quel - le
How those mer - ry girls do

bel - - - - le
eye_____ us!

Che cer - ca-no a -
We know what it

mor! Vanno a cac‑cia le don‑zel‑ ‑ ‑ ‑ ‑ ‑ ‑ ‑

means; To de‑spise us, to de‑coy_____

le, A____ cac‑cia di cor, A____ cac‑cia di cor, A cac‑

us, Like__ so man‑y queens, Like__ so man‑y queens! Like so__

(Married Women.)
2nd SOPRANOS.

‑ cia di cor!

__ man ‑ y queens!

Non ve‑de‑te che al‑le

On‑ly see the bra‑zen

Fl.

bel ‑ ‑ ‑ ‑ ‑ le Fan caccia i si‑

creat ‑ ‑ ‑ ‑ ‑ ures, With the men at

44

gnor! No - i pu - re sia - mo bel -
play! Had the lat - ter choice in feat -

le, Al _ pa - ri di lor! Al _ pa - ri di lor! Al _ pa - ri di
ures, They would turn this way, They _ would turn this way, They _ would _ turn this

1st SOPRANOS.

Si vuol pia - ce - re Ma non si
One would al - lure them, They look so

2nd SOPRANOS.

lor! Pia - cer vor - re - ste
way! If you se - cure them,

1st TENORS.

An diam!
Come here,

2nd TENORS.

Vo' ri - ma - ne - re,
No jol - ly rov - er,

1st BASSES.

Vi - va il li - quor!
Long live the wine,

Vi - va il li -
Long live the

2nd BASSES.

Vi - - va la guer - ra!
Long live the sol - dier,

№ 4. Scena, Recitative, Cavatina, and Song.

Valentine.

Siebel.

ve - ci tue può far e le fa - rà. Sia pur! Su me tu puoi con-
guard her like a broth - er in thy stead. Thine hand! Be sure I will not

tar.
fail!

Chorus.

TENORS.

Con - tar su noi dei tu.
We will watch o'er her too.

BASSES.

Con - tar su noi dei tu.
We will watch o'er her too.

Moderato.
Fl.

rall.

CAVATINA.

Valentine.

Dio pos - sen - te,
E - ven brav - est

Dio d'a-mor! Nel la-scia-re il pa--trio suol,
heart may swell In the mo-ment of farewell,

A te af-fi-do in tan--to duol,
Lov-ing smile of sis--ter kind,

La mia suo--ra, il ca--sto fior;
Qui-et home I leave be-hind,

Pro--teg-gi e gui--da-la, Ah! sì, E l'an-giol
Oft shall I think of you When-e'er the wine cup

vi--gi-le, All' al ma in-ge--nu-a
pass--es round, When a-lone my watch I keep,

ne- -li-to, Pre-ghe-rò an-co - ra_ il cie - -lo Per
fall____ me. Care-less what fate_ may_be- fall____ me, When

Tempo I.

la_____ mi - a suo - ra. Dio pos-sen - te, Dio d'a-mor!
Glo - -ry_ shall call me. Yet, the brav-est heart mayswell

Nel la-scia-re il pa - trio suol A te af-fi-do in tan-to duol
In the mo - ment of fare-well, Lov-ing_ smile of sis-ter kind

cresc.

La mia suo-ra,_ il ca-sto fior; Ah! per la suo-ra pre-ghe-rò sino all'estremo a-
Qui-et home I____ leave be-hind, Oft shall I sad-ly think of_ you when far_ a-

cresc.

p

Allegretto. **Wagner.**

nelito pre-ghe-rò!_ Andiam, partiam,
way, far a - way!_ Have done, my hearts,

Fl. & Clar.

p

11947

Song of the Golden Calf.

Tuo mi ni stro è Bel ze-
While old Mam mon leads the

bù, è Bel ze bù. Tuo mi
ball, leads off the ball; While old

ni stro è Bel ze bù, è Bel ze-
Mam mon leads the ball, leads off the

Meph.
bù: Tuo mi ni stro è Bel ze bù, è Bel ze -
ball; While old Mam mon leads the ball, While an cient

Siebel. (with Tenors)
Tuo mi ni stro è Bel ze bù, è Bel ze -
While old Mam mon leads the ball, While an cient

Wagner. (with Basses)
Tuo mi ni stro è Bel ze bù, e Bel ze -
While old Mam mon leads the ball, While an cient

№ 5. Scena and Chorus.

vo - i,   si-gno - re!   Un uom che no-to è a me, uc-ci-der-vi po - trà.
care-ful, my cap-tain!   A wea-pon that I know of is waiting for you.

Viols.

Clar. & Fag.

(snatching the glass from Wagner.)

Ai vo-stri a - mor!
I drink to you all!

cresc.

ah!   che ve - le-no è il tuo vin!   Vo-
Pah! what a rub-bish-y wine!   But

cresc.

Cornets.
dim.

Allegretto.

le - te, miei si-gno-ri, che mi-glior ve   n'of -   fra.
see if I can find you an - y bet-ter   vin -   tage!

Wind.

Meph. (striking the Bacchus - head on the sign of the Inn).

dai de - mo - ni tuoi ci__ guar - - da!
sign we bear thou canst not__ harm__ us.

dai de - mo - ni tuoi ci guar - - da!
sign we bear thou canst not harm us.

dai de - mo - ni tuoi ci__ guar - - da!
sign we bear thou canst not__ harm us.

dai de - mo - ni tuoi ci guar - - da!
sign we bear thou canst not harm us.

Tutti.

ff

Mephistopheles.

Ci ri - ve - dre - mo an - cor, miei si - gnor,__ ad -
We're sure to meet a - gain, my fine friends,__ good-

Ob. & Fag.

dim.

rir fa - ce - sti a me_____ È un va - no sor - ti -
saw as in a dream_____ Or was all an emp - ty

le - gio?
vis - ion? **Meph.** **Andantino.**

No, no, ma con - tro te la vir - tù la pro - teg - ge,
Not so,— but you may find it Not eas - y to win her!

Fl.,Ob.

Faust.

Che im - por - ta io nol vo!
What mat - ter, so I win!

E il cie - lo stes - so pu - ra la vuo - le.
Task for no sanc - ti - mo nious be - gin - ner!

vien; mi gui - da a lei d'ap - pres - so, Se no m'al - lon - ta - no da
Come, and if I can - not see her, Thy promise I'll stamp as a

Nº 6. Waltz and Chorus.

88

11947

Mephistopheles (to Faust.)

Ve - di tu que - ste bel - le, Non vuoi tu cer - car fra
How their dear eyes are beaming! On - ly see how ev -'ry

quelle, fra quel - le il tuo pia - cer?
flower is wait - ing for thee to smile.

Faust.

Ta - ci al - fin! fa tregua al tuo gar - rir, E la - scia il mio
Cease to whisper for a lit - tle while, And leave me a -

cor al suo so - - gno.
lone with my dream - - ing.

Siebel.

Passar per qui, _____ or or do - vrà
Wea - ry I wait _____ 'till she goes by

Mephistopheles.

an-cor quì! Eb - ben ca - ro mio, sie - te quà?
Not yet gone? It seemsnot,you see, Since a - gain,____

____ Ah! ah!____ dav - ver! ca - ro mio,—
____ a - gain____ we meet! Not gone yet!

sie - te quà?
not gone yet!

(Margarita crosses the stage.)
Andantino. (♩ = 69.)

Faust (approaching Margarita.)

Per - met - te - reste a me, mia bel - la da-mi-gel - la,
High-born and love-ly maid, for - give my humble du - ty,

mor_____ Lo__ veg - - go dot - tor,_____
do?_____ It would seem,_____ master mine,_____

__ soc - cor-rer do - vrò._____
__ I must teach you to woo!_____

Fl. Clar.
and Viols

cresc. __ __

f

1st group of Girls.   2nd group.

Che mai fu?   Marghe - ri-ta, Di quel gio-vin si -
What is this?   Marga - ri-ta, who would not let a

pp

104

11947

na,_____   E_____
ing,_____   Long_____

na,_____   E_____
ing,_____   Long_____

na,_____   E_____
ing,_____   Long_____

vo - lut - tà.
live the dance._____

vo - lut - tà.
live the dance._____

vo - lut - tà.
live the dance._____

End of Act II.

Act III.

№ 7. Intermezzo and Song.

Moderato, quasi Andante.

108

(plucking another flower.)

o - ra ve - diam!　ve-diam pre-sto!　So-no ap-pas - si - ti?
now I will try,　and this mo-ment!　Can it　be with-er'd?

Tempo I. Allegretto.

no!　Sa - tan　sei vin - to　già!___
No!　Thou fiend!　Thy pow'r is　gone!___

In　lor___ sol-tan-___-to ho fè:　Par-lin per　me,___
Gen-tle flow-ers, lie there,___ And　tell　her from　me,___

stacc.

Da lor le sia sve - la -　to　Il mi-se-ro___ mio　sta - to,
Long is my wea - ry　wait - ing,　Strong is my heart's wild　beat - ing,

El - la pe-nar mi　fà,___　E an - cor___　nol sa.
While to her in　the　air___　I　bend___　my　knee.___

In ques-ti fio-ri ho fè,＿＿ Par- lin per me.＿
Gen-tle flow'rs lie there＿ And tell her from me.＿

Se non ar - di - sce a - mo - re, Pos-sa in sua ve - ce il fio - re
Would she but deign to hear me, And with one smile to cheer me,

cresc. -

Sve-la-re del mio cor＿＿＿ Tut - to l'ar - dor,＿ l'ar -
For a de-light so sweet I would die at her feet,＿ I would

Fl., etc.

dim.

espress.

dor, tut - to＿ l'ar-dor, l'ar - dor, tut - to＿ l'ar-
die, would die＿ for her, I would die, would die＿ for

Ob.

Fag.

p

colla voce.

dor.＿
her.＿

f tempo.

Scena and Recitative.

cor,___ Un ba-cio le di-rà___ il re - sto.
dare!___ Were she wrong'd how_ my arm should a - venge_ her!

Se-dut - tor! ____
Brave a - ven - ger.

Or or ver - rò, ca-ro dot-tor!
Wait for me here, my learned friend.

Per te-ner com-pa - gnia   ai fior del vos-tro al - lie-vo,   Men
Since our flow'rs are laid   out   To tempt the pret-ty   maid-en   My.

vo a cer - car al - tro te - sor
gift I will ven - ture to pre - sent,

Splen - di - do più, più ric - co an -
Some - thing I ween, a lit - tle

cresc.

cor Di quan - ti mai ne vi - de in so - gno!
rar - er, To a - dorn a will - ing wear - er!

Faust.

Si, va via.
Be thou gone!

'Cello.

Meph.

Me ne vò!
I o - bey,

A - spet - ta - te - mi
But will come back a -

Viol. Clar.

cresc.

dim.

p

quì.
non.

Nº 8. Cavatina.

Faust.

Qual tur-bamento in cor mi
My ag-i-tat-ed heart's re-

sen - to,
veal - ing,

Sen-to d'a - mor ar-de-re il
The ten-der pas - sion I am

co - - re!
feel - - ing.

O Mar-ghe-ri-ta!
O Mar-ga-ri-ta!

al tuo piè vo' mo - rir!
At thy feet I fain would die!

Larghetto.

Fl.,Clar., Viol⁸ & Fag. *p cresc.*

dim.

Faust.

Sal - ve! di - mo - ra ca - sta e pu - ra,
All hail, thou dwelling pure and low - ly!

Sal - ve! di - mo - ra ca - sta e
All hail, thou dwell-ing pure and

Viol. Solo.

pu - ra. Che a me ri - ve - li__ la gen-til fan-ciul - la,
low - ly! To me the home of__ an-gel fair and ho - ly,

Che al guar - do
All mor - tal

mi - o si ce - la!
beau-ty ex-cell - ing!

Quan-ta do-vi - zia in que - sta po-ver-tà!
What wealth is here, what wealth outbidding gold,

Quan-ta do-vi - zia,
What wealth is here,__

In quest' a - sil quan-ta fe-li - ci - tà!
Of peace and love, and in-no-cence un-told!

Quan-ta do-vi - zia,
What wealth is here,__

quan-ta do-vi-zia in que - sta po-ver - tà!
of peace and love, what wealth out-bidding gold!

In quest' a -
Of peace and

Fl.
pp
Ob.

sil quan-ta fe-li - ci - tà!
love, and in-no-cence un - told!

O bei
Boun - teous

dim. col canto
Viol.

lo - chi! bei la - ri, o ve leg-giad-ra e bel - la!
Na - ture! 'twas here by day thy lore was taught her,

El - la ag-gi - rar - si suol, o - ve gen-ti - le e
Here with thy gen - tle care did'st thou o'er-shad - ow thy

snel - la, El - la per-cor - re il suol! ___
daught-er throughout the hours of the night! ___

Quì la ba-cia-va il
Here, waving tree and

so - le, E le do-ra - va il cri - - ne. Su
flow - er Made her an E - den-bow - - er Of

voi ri - vol - ger suol le lu - ci sue di -
beau - - ty and de - light; For one whose ver - y

cresc.

vi - ne Quell' an - ge-lo del ciel! Sì, quà!
birth Brought down Heav-en to our Earth! 'Twas here!

dim. pp

cresc.

sì, sì, quà!
here, 'Twas here!

dim. molto.

Sal - ve! di - mo - ra ca - sta e
All hail, thou dwelling pure and

Fl. & Clar.

pp

pu - ra,
ho - - ly!

Sal - ve! di - mo - ra ca-sta e pu - - ra, Che a me ri -
All hail, thou dwelling pure and low - - ly! To me the

ve - li la gen-til fan-ciul - la, Che al guar-do mi-o si ce -
home_ of an-gel fair and ho - ly, All mor-tal beau-ty ex-cell -
cresc.
dim.
pp
la! Sal - ve! Sal - ve! di-mo-ra ca - sta e
ing, Hail! hail! hail, thou dwelling pure and
Viol.
pu - ra, Che a me ri - ve - li la fan-
low - ly! Home of an an-gel fair and
rit. molto.
Adagio.
ciul - la che al guar-do, al guar-do mi - o si ce - - -
ho - ly, All beau - ty rare ex - cell - ing, ex - cell - - -
col canto.
pp

Meph.

più!   Che   scru-po-lo   v'as - sal?
her!   What   now can keep you   back?

ff   *p*

(sets down the casket.)

Ec-co pres - so la   so-glia   I gio - iel - li   son già: An-
On the door's qui-et   thres-hold   see, the cask - et   is   laid.   Stand

diam c'è da spe - rar._____
back! be not a - fraid!_____

Corni.

p

Nº 9. Scena and Aria.

ma - to!
sta - tion. Ob.& Clar.

Song. The King of Thule.

Moderato maestoso.

Piano.

Margarita. *un poco riten.*

"C'e - ra un re, un
"Reign'd a King in

re di Thu-lé   Che si - no a mor - te co - stan - te,
Thu - le of old   Who un-to death was true - heart - ed,

Ca - ra me-mo - ria   dell' a - man - te,   Serbò un nap-po d'or___ con
And, for the sake of   one de - part - ed, Treas-ur'd up a gob - let of

riten.

(breaking off and speaking to herself.)

se."
gold!"

A - vea mo-di gen - til a quan - to mi sembrò–
He was gen-tle in bearing, his voice too was so kind.

f   pp

(resuming the song.)

"Nes - sun ben gli fu ca - ro tan - to, nes - sun
"This rare cup so ten - der-ly cher - ish'd, This rare

ben gli fu ca - ro tan - to, E quan-te volte ai più bei
cup so ten - der-ly cher - ish'd, Aye at his side the King did

rit.

dì,— Il fi - do re se ne ser - vì
keep,— And ev-'ry time it touch'd his lip

p

Sen - tì bag-nar gli oc-chi di pian - - to!"
He wept, and thought of her long per - - ish'd."

f

"Quan - do sen-tis - si pres - so l'a - vel, Al
"O - ver the sea at last came Death! And

nap-po d'or la ma-no ste - se, Il sov-ve-nir di
on his couch, the old king ly - ing, Call'd for the cup when

lei lo pre - se, Si-no a mor - te a lei fe - del."
he was dy - ing, Al-most with his lat-est breath."

(breaking off,

Andante.

and speaking to herself.)

Io non sa-pea che dir,_ ed ar - ros-sii al - lor!_
I knew not what to answer, And blush'd like a - ny child!

(again resuming the song.)

Tempo I.

"Po - scia in o - nor del-la sua da - ma, po - scia
"Once more with the old and true de - vo - tion, Once more

in o - nor del-la sua da - ma, L'ul - ti - ma vol - ta bev-ve il
with the old and true de - vo - tion, The king would have his cup of

rit.

Più lento.

re. ___ Il nap-po al-lor gli ca - de al piè
gold. ___ Then with his hand in Death grow-ing cold,

p

L'al-ma va a al ciel che a se lo chia - - ma!"
He flung the gob-let in the o - - cean." Fl.

pp

Corni.

f

I gran si - gno - ri sol han quell' al - te - ro andar, E il par-lar lu - sin-
'Tis but to no - ble birth be-longs so brave a mien, And so ten-der with-

f

ghier!
al!

Moderato.

dolce. *cresc.* *dim.*

Andante.

Or via, non ci pen-siam! Buon Val-en-
No more, an i-dle dream! Dear Val-en-

p *f*

Andantino.

tin! se il ciel m'a-scol-ta, an-cor ti ve-drò!
tine! May Heav-en bless thee and bring thee home a-gain!

dim. *p*

Ma son quà so-la, so-la!
I am left here so lone-ly.

Tempo I.

(noticing the flowers.)

Questi fior_ Son di Sie-bel al cer-to! Com'è gen-til!
Love-ly flow'rs,_ no doubt laid there by Sie-bel, Poor faith-ful boy!

(perceiving the casket.)

Che veg-go là? On-de
But what is this? And by

quel ric-co scrigno può ve - nir? Non l'o - so toc-car,
whom can the cask-et have been left? I don't like to touch,

Ma chi sa! la chiave è là, mi par! Lo deggio a-
Tho' the key is laid be - side_ it. What is with-

prir? la man tre-ma! per - chè? A-prendo-lo non fo al - cun ma - le, mi
in? Will it o - pen? Why not? To o-pen it and take just a peep will harm

The Bijou Song.

(opens the casket.)

pa - re!
no one!

O ciel! quan-ti gio - iel! E un sogno incanta-
O Heav'n! what bril-liant gems__ 'Tis magic in their

tor e men-ti-tor__ Op-pur son de-sta? Non vi-di in vi-ta
glare de-ceives my eyes,__ Can they be re-al? O nev-er in my

mi - a ric-chez-za e-gual a que-sta!
sleep did I dream of aught so love-ly!

(Puts down the casket and kneels to

Allegro non troppo.

adorn herself with the jewels.)

Non v'è alcun; come
If I dar'd, if I

far! Pos-so al - men at-tac-car Questi be - gli o-rec
dar'd on - ly once just to try on these ear - rings so

Fl.

chi - ni!
splen - did!

Ah! Vè quì bell' e
Ah! and here by a

pron - to in fon-do al cas-set-ti - no   un cri - stal,   per po-ter mi - rar-mi in
chance with-in the love-ly cask - et   is a   glass!   Why re-sist it a - ny

es - so!   Va - na-rel-la so-no a -   - des-so?
long-er?   Why   resist it a - ny   long-er?

Allegretto.

Viols.

leggiero.

Fl. & Clar.

cresc. -

Ah! _____   E stra-
Ah! _____   the joy

più il tuo sem-bian - te, È la fi - glia d'un
chant-ment is o'er me! High-born maid - en I must

re!
be,

È la fi - glia d'un re!
High-born maid - en I must be.

Non sei più tu, Non sei più tu, ___ È la fi-glia d'un
This is not I, This is not I, ___ But it is a King's

re, che o-gnun dee sa-lu - ta - re.
daugh-ter, and all bow be - fore me!

Ah! s'e-gli quì
Ah! if it might

fos - se per co - sì ve - der - mi, Co-me u-na da-mi-
on-ly be, Ah! could he my beau-ty see. Now as a roy-al

ah! Io ri - do in po-ter me stes - sa quì ve - der!
The joy____ past compare these jew - els bright to wear!

pp   Fl.
leggiero.

ah! Io ri - do in po-ter me stes - sa quì ve - der!
Ah! the joy____ past compare these jew - els bright to wear!

Non sei tu?__ Mar - ghe - ri - ta, Non sei tu?
Was I ev - er maid - en low-ly, Is it I?

cresc.   *p*

dim-mi sù dim-mi sù, dimmi, dimmi, dì sù pre-sto! No!
come re-ply! come re-ply! Mir-ror, mirror, tell me tru-ly? No!

cresc.   *dolce.*
dim.

no! non sei più tu! no! no, non è più il tuo sem-
no, this is not I? No, Sure-ly en - chant-ment is

138

bian - te,   È la fi - - glia d'un   re!
o'er   me!   High-born maid - en I must   be,

È la fi - - glia d'un   re!   non sei più tu,
High-born maid - en I must   be,   This is not I,

cresc.

non sei più   tu ___   E la fi - glia d'un re, che ognun dee sa - lu - ta -
This is not I. ___   I am now a King's daughter and all bow be-fore

dim.

re.   Ah! s'e-gli quì   fos - se   Per co - sì ve - der - mi,
me!   Ah! if it might   on-ly be,   Ah! could he my beau-ty see,

rit.

Co - me u-na da-mi - gel - la,   Mi tro - ve - reb-be bel - la!
Now as a roy-al la - dy   He would in-deed a - dore me.

a tempo.

pp

11947

ah!_____
Ah!_____ Ah!_____

Co-me u-na da-mi-
As now a roy-al

gel-la, mi tro - ve-reb-be bel - la! Co-me u-na da-mi-
la-dy, per-chance he would a - dore me, As now a roy-al

gel-la, mi tro - ve-reb-be bel - la! Mar - ghe-
la-dy, er-chance he would a - dore___ me! Mar - ga-

ri-ta, non sei più tu, Non è più il tuo sem-
ri-ta, this is not I, Some en-chant-ment is

bian - te. No! È la fi - glia d'un
o'er___ me. No! I am now a King's

re! _____ Che o-gnun dee sa - lu - ta -
daugh - - ter, and all bow down be - fore _____

- - - - - re.
me!

№ 10. Scena and Quartet — Recitative.

(to Martha.)

ben so-no ac - col - ti i vo - stri don.) Sie-te Mar - ta Schwert-
jew-els have paved the way— for all.) I have news for your

Martha. **Meph.**

lein? Si-gnor, sì. La no - ti - zia che vi por - to, Non
ear. You have news! It af-flicts me thus to grieve you! 'Tis

Clar. & Fag.
cresc.
p Fag.
p
p

è tal da far - vi pia - cer. Il vo-stro ca - ro spo - so è
news that comes al - ways too soon. Know that your ten-der hus-band Is

f

Martha. **Margarita.** **Meph.**

mor-to, e vi sa-lu - ta! Giu-sto ciel! Che mai fu! Bah!
dead, and sends you his bless - ing! Ah! great Heav'n! What is this? Naught!

ff

Martha.

O___ ca-la-mi-
O___ dis-tressing

pp
p
pp

rì.___ Mo - ri - a! mo - ri - a! Ca - ra so - rel - la
dead! The an - gel! the an - gel lov'd me, and lov'd me

mi - a! E - ra il mio dol-ce pen-sier, E - ra il mio dol-ce pen-
on - ly! I wait-ed on her night and day, I___ waited on her night and

sier. Quan-te cure ahimè! quante pe - ne! Quan-do di lor l'al-me son
day. How I work'd for her, O, so dear-ly! But those to whom we cling most

pie - ne, La mor-te le to - glie al-lor, Quando di lor l'al-me son
near-ly, Are first to be call'd a - way; Yes, those to whom we cling most

pie - ne, La morte a noi___ le to - glie al-lor.
near - ly, Are___ the first to be call'd a - way. Fl.

dim.   pp   colla voce.   Un poco più mosso.

Non ap-pe - na gli oc-chi a-pri - a Io fa - vel - lar＿＿ do-vea con
Sure as came the dawn of morn - ing So came her call＿＿ and I must

pp

lei! E - ra l'a - mor di Mar-ghe - ri - ta! Per ve - der la mia so - rel -
go! Since she could speak she call'd me "moth-er!" O my bird! never for an-

cresc. *dim.*

Faust.

li - na, sa - prei quag - giù tut - to sof - frir. Ah! se il
oth - er, One half so tru - ly shall I care. If an -

'Cello.

ciel con un suo sor - ri - so, L'a - ves - se fat-ta e gua - le a
oth - er so like an an - gel, So＿ per - fect, so like thee could

11947

Recitative.*

Adagio.

Not - te,   sten - di   su lor   l'om - bra
O   night,   draw   round a - bout   them thy

tu - - a,   A - mor, _____   chiu - dii lor
cur - - tain,   Let   naught _____   wak - en sus -

co - ri   al   ri - mor - - so im - por -
pi - cion   Or   mis - giv - - ing a -

tun, _____ E voi fior' d'o - lez zo sot -
rouse, _____ Ye flow'rs, with your o - dor so

til, tut - ti vi fac - cia a - prir la mia man ma - le -
sweet, aid the en - tranc - ing charm and her sens-es be -

det - ta, Più non tur - ba - te il cor di Mar - ghe -
wil - - der, Let her be - lieve her-self dream-ing in

ri - - - - - ta.
Heav - - - - en.

Nº 11. Duet.

vi - so,   Dammi ancor contem - plar_ il tuo vi - - - -
fore me,   Let me gaze on the vis - ion be - fore_____

so,   Al pal - li - do chiar-or___ Che vien dame,   While from yon e - ther blue___ Look how the

Horns.

gli a-stri d'or,___ e___ posa un lie - ve - ve - lo   Sul
star of eve___ Bright and ten-der lin - gers o'er   me   To

Fl.   Horns.   Ob.

Margarita.

vol - to,   sul vol-to tuo sì bel.   O si - len - zio!
love,___   to love thy beau - ty too!   O what rapt - ure!

Viols.

pp

o mi-ster!   i - nef-fa - bil mi-ste - ro!   vo - lut-ta - de dol-
like a spell   Does the ev'n-ing en-chant me!   With a ra - diance mys-

Non sai tu___ com'è fe_li_ce a_ mar?___ A-
In that spell__ de_fy what Fate can do. ___ In

mar! ___ por_ _ tar in cor un ar_
love ___ no mor_ tal pow'r Faith_ful

dor o_gnor fer_ven_ _te!
heart from heart can sev_ _er,

In _ neb_bri_ar_si an_ cor da_
What _ _ e'er the weal or woe, We'll

mor e_ter_na_men_ _te!
faith _ _ _ ful be for ev_ _er!

172

Adagio.

Sempre amar!
Ev - er true!

Sempre, sempre!
Ev - er faithful!

Sempre amar!
Ev - er true!

Sempre, sempre!
Ev - er faithful!

Adagio.

Clar.

Fag.

Faust.

Not - te d'a - mor tut - ta splen - dor,— Begli a - stri d'o - ro O ce -
O ten - der moon,— O star - ry Heav'n, Si - lent a - bove thee, Where the

Viols.

Horns & 'Celli.

le - ste vo - lut - tà!— U - dir - si dir: t'a - mo, t'a - mo, t'a - do - ro.
an - gels are en - thron'd Hear, as I swear, how dear - ly do I love thee.

Marg.

Ti vo - glio a - mar,— i - do - la - trar! Par - la an - co - ra! Io tuo sa -
Yet once a - gain,— be - lov - ed one, Let me hear thee; It is but

11947

rò, sì, t'a - do - ro, Per te vo - gl'io mo - rir!____
life to be near thee, thine own, and thine a - lone!____

Marg.

Par - la, parla an-co-ra! Ah! sì, t'a-
Speak, love! let me hear thee! Ah! my be-

Fl., Clar., etc.

ppp

do - ro, Per te vo - gl'io morir, per te vogl'io mo-rir!____
lov - ed! I am thine own! I am thine own, and thine a - lone.____

rit.

Allegro agitato.   Marg.

Ah! va via!   Ah! va
Ah be - gone!   Ah! be -

Faust.

Mar - ghe - ri - ta!   Mar - ghe - ri - ta!
Mar - ga - ri - ta!   Mar - ga - ri - ta!

Allegro agitato.

f p   *fp*

174

11947

176

Margarita.

chie-do per___ pie - tà! Ad-dio! Ad-dio! sì, va via
mer-cy to___ be-gone! A-dieu, A-dieu, let me en-

Tu vuoi, ahi-mè, che t'ab-ban-
Thou seest, ah me, how I en-

pre - sto, va via, io tre - mo, pie - tà! pie -
treat you, be-gone! I trem - ble, I faint with

do - ni, Ahi qual do - lor! ahi qual do -
treat thee, Let me re - main, let me re -

ta! Il cor non fran - ge - re di Mar - ghe -
fear! Pit - y and spare the heart of Mar - ga -

lor! Tu mi spez - zi il
main. If in - deed thou dost

ri - ta! Il cor non fran - ge - re di Mar - ghe -
ri - ta! Pit - y and spare the heart of Mar - ga -

cor!___ Tu mi spez - zi il
love me, If in - deed thou dost

(Margarita opens her window.)

Larghetto.

Clar. Ob. Ve- Be-

pp

Horns.

de - te! a - pre la sua fi-
hold now! There she o - pens the

poco cresc.

Margarita.

ne - stra. Fl. Ei
win - dow. He

dim. pp dolcissimo.

m'a - ma! ei m'a - ma! Tur- ba-to è il mio
loves me! He loves me! Re-peat it a-

cor! L'augel - lo can - ta,
gain, O bird, that call - - est,

Ob. Fl.

è ques - ta l'e - sta - si__ d'a - mor,__   Tut - to d'a-
Full of the ver - y breath of Love!__   See how the

mo - re si ri - con - si - glia.   Do - man,__ do-
boughs em-brace as they mur - mur!   At morn!__ at

cresc.

man,__   ah! a tor - nar t'at-
morn!__   Ah! speed thou night a-

fret - ta o mio te - sor!   sì!__
way, He will re - turn!   come!__

cresc. molto.

vien!__   ah! **Meph.**
Come!__ **Faust.**   ah!

Mar - ghe - ri - ta!   Hein!__
Mar - ga - ri - ta!   There! Ha! ha! ha! ha! ha!

End of Act III.

Act IV.
Intermezzo and Recitative.

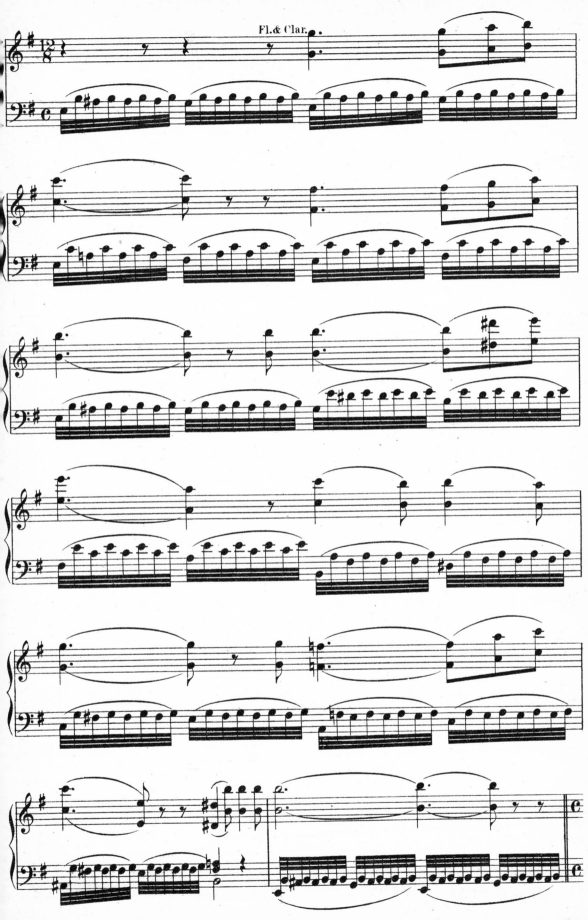

188

N⁰ 12. Scena.— The Spinning-wheel Song.

Na-sco-se e-ran là, le cru-de-li!
They mock in my face! ah! how cru-el!

Io non tro-
I, too, have

va-va al-lor ol-trag-gio, per pu-nir l'er-ror dell' al-tre
censured with all my bit-ter-ness, And have mock'd the frail-ties of the

don-ne, or non tro- vo pie-tà per l'er-ror ch'io com-
oth-ers, And to- day, when my own sin might meet with some

mi-si. Sul ca-po mi-o l'on-ta piom-bò!
pit-y, I pray to them for mer-cy in vain!

Ahi! ma pur
Yet, in-deed,

Dio lo sa io non mi re-si in-fa- me, Ma
Heav-en knows, Al-tho' I am not stain- less, 'Twas

11947

so - lo _ per a - mo - re, col - pe - vo - le   fu _ i _ per a -
by no _ pas - sion shame - less, But Love, ten - der   Love led _ me a -

(♩ = 72.)

mor!
stray!

Fag.

pp

Horns.

r.h.

Moderato.

1st Viol.   2nd Viol.   1st Viol.   2nd Viol.

pp

Ei   non tor - ha an - cor, _____   ei   non torna an -
He   will not re - turn, _____   He   will not re -

191

11947

so- - -la, Que- sto a- ma- ro pian - to fos- se no - to al-
lone!_____ Could my bit- ter grief on- ly be known,_____ ah

cresc.

a piacere.

men!_____ oh! do - - ve s'ag - gi - ra? ei non tor - na an-
me!_____ O where_____ is he roam - ing? Will he not re-

dim.   pp

cor!_____ Ma_____ se al-
turn?_____ But_____ once

men_____ ve - der_lo e u - dir_ lo an - co - ra, con - ces - so mi
more,_____ once more to be- hold and to hear him, How much do I

cresc. -

fos - se e strin - ger-lo al co - re! ei non tor - na an-
yearn!_____ once more_____ to em - brace him, Will he not re-

cor!_____ ei non tor -na an -cor! Oh mio Si - gnor, Oh mio Si -
turn?_____ will he not re - turn? O—my lord!_____ O—my

Allegro.

gnor_____ mio a - mo - - re! rive - der ti an -
lord!_____ my lov - - er! If I could but

ff Wind.

co - ra, rive-den - ti an - co - ra, ed ab-brac-ciar - ti!
see thee, If I could but see thee, but em - brace thee!

Tempo I.

Ah vien!_____ ah
Ah me!_____ ah

pp 3

vien!_____ Oh do - ve s'ag - gi - ra? ei non tor - na an -
me!_____ O where is he roam - ing? He will not__ re -

cor!
turn!

pp

Scena and Recit.

Siebel. (approaching quickly).

Marghe -
Marga -

p

cresc. - -

f

Margarita. Siebel. Margarita.

ri - ta! Sie - bel! Piange-te an - cor! Ahi-mè! sol voi non sie-te a me cru -
ri - ta! Sie - bel! A - gain in tears? Ah, me! you on - ly do not ask my

cer - ta son ch'ei m'a - ma, Ahi - mè!___ ma quel -l'om bra a lùi vi -
well I know he loves me, A - las!___ But that shad - ow at his

cin,___ quel-l'uom co - sì mal-va - gio, che ri - dea tut - to in
side,___ That cold e - vil man___ who mocks at all we

cui crediam; Qua-leun fan-ta-sma lo se - gue e mai la-sciar-lo
trust in Clings to him like a ghost,___ And will not set him

vuol E - gli è che a me strappa il mio a - mor, e per
free. 'Tis he who bears my love from me And for

cui son vil-men-te abban-do - na - ta Pres-so il fan-ciul che calmo ri - po-
whom I am base - ly de - serted; Near, when a child, calmly lay a-

198

11947

li - ce, pian-gi in - fe - li - ce, io pian-ge-rò, io pian-ge-rò con
me, too, mournful the day!___ Hope and de - light have pass'd from life a-

tè.
way!

Qua - li due fio-ri su l'is-tes - so ste - lo Ta - le il de-
We were not born with true love to tri - fle! Nor born to

stin u - ni - va i no - stri cor; Se ri - co - pri l'a - man - te un ne-ro
part because the wind blows cold: What tho' the storm the summer garden

ve - lo, o Mar-ghe-ri-ta, o Mar-ghe-ri - ta, io ti sa-rò fe-de-le ami-co o-
ri - fle, O Mar-ga-ri - ta! O Mar-ga-ri - ta! Still on the bough is left a leaf of

gnor,   ti sa - rò fe - de - le a - mi - co o - gnor,   ti sa -
gold,   On the bough is left a leaf of gold,   on the

rò fe - de - le a - mi - co o - gnor.
bough is left a leaf of gold.

Moderato.
Marg.

V'as - si - sta Id - di '- o,   mer - cè vi ren - da il cie - lo,
May Heav'n re - ward thee, friend,   For all thine aid to me, ___

Clar.

Viola.

Fag.

I cru - di che mol - trag - gia - no, non pon - no   Chiu - der le por - te a
Those who, by right of vir - tue, now dis - dain me   Give me but lit - tle

Viol?

me   del tem - pio del Si - gnor!   V'an - drò pel fi - glio mio, e per
pain   While I have pow'r to pray!   I go be - fore the Cross   My re -

Clar.

41947

lui a pre-gar! ___
pen-tance to lay. ___

Viol?, Fl., & Cl.

dim. _pp_

cresc.

Siebel.

Allegro molto.

_ff_

Mar - ta!
Mar - tha!

Martha.

Lo - de al ciel, sei tu   Do-v'è Marghe-ri - ta?   El - la
Now Heav'n be prais'd, 'tis you!   Where is Mar-ga - ri - ta?   Lit - tle

_p_   _p_   _cresc. molto._ -

Siebel.

O ciel! Va-len-tino!
O Heav'n! Va-len-tine!

non sa suo fra-tel è ar-ri - va-to.
knows she that her broth-er is come.

Nº 13. The Soldiers' Chorus.

206

a - spet - tar,____

not de - plore! ____

a - spet - tar,____

not de - plore! ____

a - spet - tar, ____

not de - plore! ____

Fl., Clar., Cornet, etc.

De - po - niam il bran - do,

Fold_ the flag, my broth - ers!

De - po - niam il bran - do,

Fold the flag, my broth - ers!

De - po - niam il bran - do,

Fold the flag, my broth - ers!

De - po - niam_ il bran - - do.

Fold_ the flag,_ my broth - - ers!

De - po - niam il bran - - do.

Fold the flag, my broth - - ers!

De - po - niam il bran - - do.

Fold the flag, my broth - - ers!

11947

Animato.

_ pre - ga. Dio per me. La gen-til! Co-me atten - ta sa -
_ ing to Heav'n for me! Gen-tle girl, Fan - cy how she will.

rà, quan-do m'u-drà nar - ra - re, Quan-to in guer - ra o-prai fi -
lend ea - ger and rapt at - ten - tion, To the tale___ I have to

cresc.
f

nor. _____
tell! _____

f Allegro.
rit.

1ST TENORS.
f   3   pp
Sì, fa piacer nel-la fa - mi - glia, Di narrar al fanciul, che
Yes! 'tis a joy for men vic - to - rious To the lads by the fire-light

2ND TENORS.
f   3   pp
Sì, fa piacer nel-la fa - mi - glia, Di narrar al fanciul, che
Yes! 'tis a joy for men vic - to - rious To the lads by the fire-light

BASSES.
f   3   pp
Sì, fa piacer nel-la fa - mi - glia, Di narrar al fanciul, che
Yes! 'tis a joy for men vic - to - rious To the lads by the fire-light

a tempo.
f   3   3   pp

del suo pa - dre è al - ter,
trem - bling in our arms,

Al - la spo - - sa ed al - la
To our wives and to our

fi - glia,
chil - - dren,

L'im - pre - - se del guer-
To talk of war's a -

rier, l'im-pre - se, l'im-pre - se del guer-rier!
larms! its bat - tles, to talk of war's a - larms!

- po il no-stro ac-ciar,____ Per te noi pu-gniam, per te noi pu-gniam, Per
- if a-lone, or last?____ And boast he was true, as cow-ard might do when

te ____ tri - on - fiam. ____ Oh glo - ria
per - il is past? ____ Glo - ry and

cin - ta d'al - lor, d'al - lor, ____ Non hai ri -
love to the men of old! ____ Their sons may

va - le nel no - stro cor, ____ Di - spie - ga
cop - y their vir - tues bold, ____ Cour - age in

l'a - le sul vin - ci - tor,___ Ac - cen - di nei cor no - vel - lo va-
heart and a sword in hand,___ All read - y to fight for Fa - - ther-

l'a - le sul vin - ci - tor,___ Ac - cen - di nei cor no - vel - lo va-
heart and a sword in hand,___ All read - y to fight for Fa - - ther-

lor.___ Ver___ la ma-
land.___ Now___ to home a-

lor.___ Ver___ la ma-
land.___ Now___ to home a-

Clar. Horns, etc.

Saxhorns, Fag., etc.

gion___ or ci af - fret - tiam Ci a-spet - tan là, fatta è la
gain___ we come, the long and fie - ry strife of bat - tle

gion___ or ci af - fret - tiam Ci a-spet - tan là, fatta è la
gain___ we come, the long and fie - ry strife of bat - tle

pa - ce! _____ Non _____ più in du -
o - ver; _____ Rest _____ is pleas - ant

pa - ce! _____ Non _____ più in du -
o - ver; _____ Rest _____ is pleas - ant

giam, _____ a che tar - dar! Ver la ma - gion or ci af - fret -
af - - ter toil as hard as ours be - neath a stran - ger

giam, _____ a che tar - dar! _____ or ci af - fret -
af - - ter toil be - neath _____ a stran - ger

tiam, _____ O - - gnu - no
sun. _____ Man - - y a maid - en

tiam, Ver la ma - gion or ci af - fret - tiam _____ O - gnu - no
sun, Be - neath a wild and stran - ger sun. _____ The maid - en

cresc.

p

qui_____ ci ab-brac - ce - rà, A-mor c'in-vi-ta, a-mor ci a-
fair_____ is wait-ing here to greet her tru-ant sol-dier-

1st BASSES.

qui_____ ci ab-brac - ce - rà, A-mor c'in-vi-ta, a-mor ci a-
fair_____ is wait-ing here to greet her tru-ant sol-dier-

2nd BASSES.

rà, A-mor c'in-vi-ta, a-mor ci a-
here to greet her tru-ant sol-dier-

spet - ta, _____ E più d'un cor _____ pal-pi - te -
lov - er, _____ And man-y a heart _____ will fail, and

spet - ta, _____ E più d'un cor _____ pal-pi - te -
lov - er, _____ And man-y a heart _____ will fail, and

spet - ta, _____ E più d'un cor pal-pi - - te and
lov - er, _____ And man-y a heart will fail, _____ and

rà, _____ pal-pi - te rà, _____ Il no-stro
brow _____ grow pale to hear, _____ to hear the

rà, _____ pal-pi - te rà, _____ Il no-stro
brow _____ grow pale to hear, _____ to hear the

rà, pal-pi - - te rà, pal-pi - - te
brow grow pale _____ to hear, to hear _____ the

cresc.

dim.　　　　　　　　　　　p　　　　　　cresc.

dir,　il no-stro dir stan-do ad u - dir,＿＿＿＿＿　A - mor ci a
tale　of cru - el per - il he has　run,＿＿＿＿＿　And man - y a

dir,　il no-stro dir stan-do ad u - dir,＿＿＿＿＿　A - mor ci a-
tale　of cru - el per - il he has　run,＿＿＿＿＿　And man - y a

dir,　il no-stro dir stan-do ad u - dir,　A - mor＿＿＿ ci a
tale　of cru - el per - il he has run,　And man＿＿＿ y a

dim.　　　　　　　　　　　　cresc.

spet - ta,＿＿＿＿＿　E più d'un cor pal-pi-te-rà, pal-pi te-
heart,＿＿＿＿＿＿　and man - y a heart will fail, and brow grow pale　to

spet - ta,＿＿＿＿＿　E più d'un cor pal-pi-te-rà, pal-pi te-
heart,＿＿＿＿＿＿　and man - y a heart will fail, and brow grow pale　to

spet - ta, E più d'un cor pal-pi-te-rà, pal-pi-te-rà, pal-pi te-
heart, a heart will fail, and man - y a heart will fail, and brow grow pale to

f　　　　　　dim.　　　　　　p

rà,　Il no - stro dir stan-do ad u - dir,＿＿＿＿　Or ci af-fret-
hear the tale　of per - il he has run.＿＿＿＿　We are at

rà,　Il no - stro dir stan-do ad u - dir,＿＿＿＿　Or ci af - fret-
hear the tale　of per - il he has run.＿＿＿＿　We are at

rà,　Il no - stro dir stan-do ad u - dir,＿＿＿＿　Or ci af - fret-
hear the tale　of per - il he has run.＿＿＿＿　We are at

Viol.

f　　　　　　dim.　　　　　　p

lor_____ ac - cen - di nei cor!_____
die_____ for Fa - -ther - land!_____

lor_____ ac - cen - di nei cor!_____
die_____ for Fa - -ther - land!_____

Recitative.

Nº 14. Scena and Serenade.

val do-po a - ver - la la - scia-ta? Il no-stro a-spet - to sa-ria più gra-to al-
gain, Af - ter once hav-ing left her? I know of beau-ties as fresh, and far more

Faust.

tro - - ve, Al sab - ba - to n'an - diam! Mar-ghe-
kind - - ly, And wait-ing but for you! Mar-ga-

Horns.

f

Meph.

ri - ta! Or-mai l'av - vi - so mio non val con - tro la
ri - ta! I see that I may talk in vain, Since, like a

p

cresc.

vo - stra vo - glia!— Ma per — non re - star al - la
fool, you love her. But to un - close yon-der door We must

dim.

p

p

so - glia, La vo - ce mia do - vrà per voi far - si a - scol -
move her. Just list - en while I sing her a fan - ci - ful

226

Allegretto.
(Throwing back his cloak, and accompanying himself on the guitar.)

Un poco più lento.

11947

Ma l'a - mi - co fa - vo - ri - to, Ma l'a - mi - co fa - vo -
To his mis-tress dear, while creep - ing, To his mis-tress dear, while

ri - to, Ri - ce - ver non val. Ah! ah! ah!
creep - ing, Thus sang her cav - a - lier! Ha! ha! ha!

ah! ah! ah! ah! ah! ah! ah! Se non t'ha pria mes - so al
ha! ha! ha! ha! ha! ha! ha! Ere the tell - tale moon had

di - to, L'a - nel - lo nu - zial, Se
ris - en, A bird of night thus did sing Lock

_ non t'ha pria mes-so al di - to, L'a - nel nu - zia - le, l'a - nel nu -
_ thy heart like a - ny pris-on, Till thou se - cur - est a wed - ding-

zial.
ring.

Faust: Tacer non vuoi tu!
Faust: Be silent, I tell thee!

Fl., Ob., & Clar.

Ca-te-ri-na es-ser cru - de - le, tan - to cru-del,
Cat-a-ri - na is so cru - el, Such a cru-el miss,

Fl. & Ob.

Viols.

p stacc.

non_ vuol, non vuol, Da ne-gar al suo fe - del, Un so-lo ba-cio, un
too_ cru-el miss, To a mortal bending low-ly, not to grant a

so - lo, al suo fe - del, Ma l'a-mi-vo fa-vo-ri - to,
kiss, just a par-don kiss, Sang the pen-i -tent so slow - ly,

dim.

Viols. Ob.

Ma l'a-mi-co fa-vo-ri - to, Ri - ce - - ver non
Sang the pen-i - tent so slow - ly, That naught could be a -

riten.

Nº 15. The Duel.

Trio.

Valentine.

Che fa - te
What is your

qui, si - gnor?___
will with me?___

Per - don!
With you,

mio ca - me -
my cap - tain

Mephistopheles.

ra   - ta,
splen - did?

per - don!
with you?

Non è di - ret - ta a
Our hum - ble ser - e -

Valentine.

voi,   la nostra se - re - na - ta! Mia so - rel-   -la, l'u -
nade   was not for you in - tend - ed! At my sis-   -ter, my

(Valentine shatters
Mephistopheles' guitar.)

Faust.   Meph.

dri - a me-glio di me.   Oh ciel!   Perchè voi vi sde-
sis - ter You then would jeer. Oh heav'n! Is there some - thing that

Viola.

Valentine.

gna - te,   La   no - stra canzon voi non a - ma - te? Tre-gua all'ol-
bites you?   Or,   may be, no ser-e - nade de - lights you? E - nough of

trag - - gio,   or - mai!   A chi di voi degg' io chie-der ra-
in - - sult.   Re - ply!   By which of you two shall I be re-

Viola.

V'cello.

gio - ne   Del di - so - nor,   che   su me
quit - ed   For name de - fil'd,   for   lau - rel

ca - - de?   Chi di voi du - - e sve - nar qui do-
blight - ed?   Which of you two shall be thrust by my

947

234

11947

(Grasping the charm suspended round his neck.)

Valentine.

E tu, che mi sal-va-sti o-
Thou charm! on which to shield my

gnor,_____ Tu, che mi die-de Mar-ghe-ri-
life,_____ Frail Mar-ga-ri-ta's pra'yrswerespo-

ta, Non ti vo' più, ti get-to via, Non ti vo'
ken, I will not have thee in the strife, I will not

più, ti get-to via,_____ Me-da- -glia o-
have thee in the strife_____ Be- gone, ac-cur'sd

cresc.

(2nd thrust.)

ff

fp

(3rd thrust.)

ff

(Valentine falls.)

(4th thrust.)

Horn.

ff

p

Meph.

Ed ec-coil no-stro e - ro - e di - ste-so e-san-gue al suo - lo.
So, Captain, lie you there! On your last bed of glo - ry!

O - ra fug-gir dob-biam, fug - giam!__
We must hur - ry a - way! Come quick - ly!

cresc.

Nº 16. The Death of Valentine.
Chorus.

vien, Ciac - co - stiam, ciac - co - stiam, soc - cor - rer - gli con
head; To his aid, to his aid, Sup - port him, raise his

vien. Ciac - co - stiam, ciac - co - stiam, soc - cor - rer - gli con
head; To his aid, to his aid, Sup - port him, raise his

vien, Ciac - co - stiam, ciac - co - stiam, soc - cor - rer - gli con
head; To his aid, to his aid, Sup - port him, raise his

f

un poco riten.

Valentine.

Non val, non val, per - chè mai far tan - ti la -
Too late! too late! There's no need, good friends, to be-

vien.
head.

vien.
head.

vien.
head.

Viols.

p

un poco riten.

'Cello.

men - ti, Trop - po vid' io la mor - te in vi - so, per te -
wail me! Too oft - en have I look'd on Death to be a-

Clar. & Fag.

tr

dim.

sfz

Margarita (appears at back.)

mer quand' es - sa vie-ne_a me.   Va-len - tin!   Va-len-
fraid at   last when he is near!   Val-en - tine!   Val-en-

Valentine.

tin! _____ Mar-ghe - ri - ta!   eb - ben   che bra - mi
tine! _____ Mar-ga - ri - ta!   What now?   Why art thou

Margarita.

O   Di - o!
Oh   Heav - en!

Io   mo - ro   per
Thy shame hath de -

tu!   va via!
here?   Be - gone!

le - i,   Stol - to dav - ver vol - li sfi - da - re_il se - dut -
stroy'd me!   Her fine se - du - cer's sword Hath sent her broth - er

Tu   mor - rai   tra cen - ci
Thou,   thou too,   dy - ing   must

vil,   Io   mo - ro per te   co -
lie!   Ah!   Thy hand hath slain me, Like a

me un sol - da - to   muor!
Sol - dier thus I   die!

Lento, e sotto voce.

SOPRANOS. (Siebel and Martha with SOPR.)   pp

Che il Si - gno - re l'ac - col - ga pie - to - so nel suo
Heav'n give him rest! and ac - cord her for - give - ness for her

TENORS.

Che il Si - gno - re l'ac - col - ga pie - to - so nel suo
Heav'n give him rest! and ac - cord her for - give - ness for her

BASSES.

Che il Si - gno - re l'ac - col - ga pie - to - so nel suo
Heav'n give him rest! and ac - cord her for - give - ness for her

Lento, e sotto voce.

No 17. Church Scene.

Margarita. (kneeling down by the holy-water font.)

Si - gnor, con - ces - so
O Thou! who on Thy

si - a all' u - mil vostr' an - cel - la di __ pro - strar - si all' al - tar. __
throne givest ear un - to re - pentance, Here, __ at Thy feet, let me pray! __

Organ.

(The tomb opens, and discoveres Mephistopheles, who bends toward Margarita's ear.)

Meph.

Org.

chia - ma! l'infer - no sua ti vuol!____ È l'e - ter - no do -
low call to bid thee to their home!____ Worms to welcome, and

lor, è l'e-ter-na sven-tu - ra, è l'e - ter - no pe -
fire ev-er-last ing to warm thee! Wait un - til thou shalt

nar!____ Ciel! che
come!____ Ah! what

Margarita.

Organ. Orch.

vo - ce o - do mai, chi mi par - la nell' om - bra? Pie - to - so ciel,
sound in the gloom Is be - neath me, a - round me? Angels of wrath,

qual vo - ce cu - pa scen - de su me!____
Is this your sentence of cru - el doom?____

Chorus of Priests and Boys (behind the scenes.)

SOPRANOS, TENORS and BASSES.

Quan - do di Dio il dì ver - rà,___
When the book shall be un - seal - ed,___

La cro - ce in ciel ri-splen - de - rà,___
When the fut - ure be re - veal - ed,___

Il mon - do in - ter ro - vi - ne - rà,___
What shall fal - len, fal - len mor-tals see___

Margarita.

Ahi-mè! ahi - mè!___ il sa-cro can - to è più tre-men - do an -
And I, the frail - est of the frail Have most need of your for -

Meph.

co - ra! No!_____ per te, Dio non ha più per -
give - ness! No!_____ not now! let them weep, But thy

11947

End of Act IV.

Act V.

Intermezzo and Recitative.

Dorme il cu-sto-de, ec-co le chia-vi, or va, Che la tua man schiuda le
The warder slumbers, The keys are here. Her life is in your hands, and you must

Faust.

Eb-ben, va!
Get you gone!

por-te.
save her.

Non tar-dar!
No de-lay!

Adagio

di fuo-ri io ve-glie-
out-side the door I

pp colla voce

rò.
wait!

№ 18. Duet.

me u-na vi - le de-lin-quen - te,   For-se il do-lor
if her-self,___ not I, were guilt - - y.   Grief and affright___

dim.   p

___ le tur-bò la ragion.   Il suo bambin,
___have her reason destroy'd. Clar.   Our lit-tle child—

p   cresc.

o ciel!   Uc - cise il suo bam-bin, di propria ma - no!
O Heav'n!   slain at its birth by her In sudden mad - ness!

f   dim. 'Cello.

Margarita.
Recit.

f   sf

Marghe - ri - ta!   Marghe - ri - ta!   Ah! La sua vo-ce al cor suo-
Marga - ri - ta!   Marga - ri - ta!   Ah! do I hear thee once a-

f. *Moderato.*

nò,   A quel-la vo-ce il cor si ria-ni - mò.
gain,   Thou darling voice of days long gone by.

Faust.

Marghe-ri - ta!
Mar-ga-ri - ta!

Viols.

pp

Allegro.   Faust.

cor!___   Sì,   ma,   vien!   vien! l'o - ra
love!___   Yes!   but   come!   Come! time is

pas - - - sa!   Vien!
pass - - - ing!   Come!

vien!   fug-giam di quà!   non tar - diam!___   ci affret-
come!   we must a - way!   They will soon___   come to

tia - mo!   L'al - ba già schia - ra il ciel,
claim   thee!   Yon - der the dawn   is   grey,

il   palco è gia   le - va - to!   Già vien l'o - ra fa -
Think of the doom   that waits   thee With hour of   ear - ly

rir do-vrò, tu sol_ vi-ver de- - - vi! Ahi -
die! Farewell! My mem-'ry live to cher- - - ish! Ah!

mè! qual tor-mem- - - to! Ah
me! this is an- - - guish! But

no! ah no! L'or-ren-do fa - to non sa-rà com-
no! but no! The fear-ful scaf-fold shall not, shall not

pi- - to! Sot - trar-ti sa - prò, mio te -
have thee! For ev - er now, Come what, come

sor, Al sup - pli - - zio ab - bor -
may! From such death _____ I will

№ 19. Trio and Finale.

Finale.

Cri - sto ri - na-scean - co - ra!
Let Earth be ev - er cru - el,

Cri - sto ri - su - sci-
Heav'n is for - giv -

Cri - sto ri - na-scean - co - ra!
Let Earth be ev - er cru - el,

Cri - sto ri - su - sci-
Heav'n is for - giv -

Cri - sto ri - na-scean - co - ra!
Let Earth be ev - er cru - el,

Cri - sto ri - su - sci-
Heav'n is for - giv -

Org.

Orch.

3

Org.

tò!
ing!

tò!
ing!

tò!
ing!

cresc.

Org. and Orch.

dim.

pp

8va bassa

End of the Opera.

Faust.

Ballet.

Allegretto, Mouvement de Valse.

Moderato maestoso.

Moderato con moto.

5.

Allegro vivo.

7.

324

11947

325

11947